SPACE ENCYCLOPEDIA

PLANETS

An imprint of Om Books International

Contents

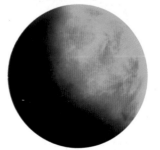

PLANETS

▲ *A captivating view of the Sun and the planets that form the solar system.*

Our solar system consists of eight planets. Mercury, the closest planet to the Sun, is only a bit larger than Earth's moon. Venus, the second planet from the Sun, is terribly hot. Earth is the third planet from the Sun; two-thirds of this planet is covered with water and it is the only planet known to harbour life. Mars, the fourth planet, is a reddish planet that is cold and dusty.

Jupiter, the fifth planet, is the largest planet in the solar system. Saturn, the sixth planet, is known for its rings. The seventh planet, Uranus, is the only giant planet that orbits on its side. Neptune, the eighth planet, is known for strong winds. Until 2006, Pluto was considered to be a planet but was later demoted to a dwarf planet.

Mercury

Mercury is the smallest planet in our solar system. Of the eight planets, it is the planet closest to the Sun.

Mercury is named after the Roman deity Mercury, the messenger of the gods.

Mercury

Mass: 330,104,000,000,000 billion kg (0.055 x Earth)

Equatorial diameter: 4879

Equatorial circumference: 15,329 km

Notable moons: None

Orbit period: 87.97 Earth days

Surface temperature: -173 °C to 427 °C

Internal structure

Mercury consists of approximately 70 per cent metallic and 30 per cent silicate material. Mercury's density is the second highest in the solar system at 5.427 g/cm³. Geologists estimate that its core occupies about 42 per cent of its volume. In addition, its crust is believed to be 100–300 km thick.

Surface geology

Mercury possesses a "dorsa" or "wrinkle-ridges", moon-like highlands, montes (mountains), planitiae (plains), rupes (escarpments) and valles (valleys). There are craters on Mercury, which range in diameter from small bowl-shaped cavities to multi-ringed impact basins, 100 km wide. "Caloris Basin", with its diameter of 1,550 km, is the largest known crater .The impact that resulted in the Caloris basin, was very powerful. It triggered lava eruptions and left a concentric ring over 2-km tall around the impact of the crater.

An image of the planet Mercury as captured by a space probe of NASA. It appears red because it is covered in red soil.

The surface of the planet Mercury is very similar to that of the moon in the sense that it is rough and full of craters and rocks. It is also dry and dusty seeing that it is the closest planet to the Sun.

Atmosphere

The surface temperature of Mercury ranges from 100 K to 700 K at the most extreme places. The subsolar point reaches about 700 K during perihelion (when Earth is closest to the Sun), but only 550 K at aphelion (when Earth is farthest from the Sun). On the dark side of the planet, the temperatures average at about 110 K.

Magnetic field and magnetosphere

Despite its small size and slow 59-day-long rotation, Mercury has a significant magnetic field. Like that of Earth, Mercury's magnetic field is bipolar (magnetic poles of equal magnitude and opposite signs). Space probes have indicated that the strength and shape of the magnetic field are stable.

FUN FACT

Mercury is only the second hottest planet in the solar system despite being the closest to the Sun, with the hottest planet being Venus.

Location and Movement

Mercury has the most eccentric orbit among all the planets. It takes 87.969 Earth days to complete an orbit. Its higher velocity when it is near perihelion is clear from the greater distance it covers at each five-day interval.

Mercury's orbit and axis

Mercury's orbit is inclined by seven degrees to the plane of Earth's orbit. Its axial tilt is almost zero. From certain points on the surface of Mercury, one would be able to see the Sun rising halfway, then reversing and setting before rising again. All this would happen within the same day on Mercury. To a hypothetical observer on Mercury, the Sun appears to move in a backward direction.

Unlike the moon whose one side faces Earth at all times, Mercury's rotation causes it to turn one and a half times for every revolution around the Sun.

Longitude convention

The longitude convention for Mercury puts the zero of its longitude at one of the two hottest points on the surface. The two hottest places on the equator are at longitudes 0° W and 180° W, and the coolest points on the equator are at longitudes 90° W and 270° W.

The planet has a 3:2 spin-orbit resonance, rotating thrice for every two revolutions around the Sun.

Spin-orbit resonance

For many years, it was believed that this planet was tidally locked with the Sun at the same time, rotating once for each orbit and always keeping the same face directed towards the Sun, similar to the way that the same side of the moon always faces Earth. However, this is not true. It rotates thrice for every two revolutions around the Sun.

Observation

Observing Mercury is complicated due to its proximity to the Sun, as it is difficult to distinguish it in the Sun's glare. It can be observed for only a brief period either in the morning or evening twilight. Additionally, it can be seen during a total solar eclipse. Like the Moon and Venus, it exhibits phases as seen from Earth.

FUN FACT

Just like humans, Mercury too has wrinkles. The wrinkles on its surface were caused because of the cooling and contracting of the iron core. Scientsts have referred to these wrinkles as "lobate scarps". These scarps can be up to 1.6 km high and hundreds of km long.

Venus

The planet, second from the Sun is Venus. After the moon, it is the second brightest object seen in the night sky. It never appears to venture far from the Sun. It can also be seen during daytime from the Earth. It is almost the same size as Earth and is also referred to as Earth's twin. This planet is named after the Roman goddess of love and beauty because of its brightness.

Venus

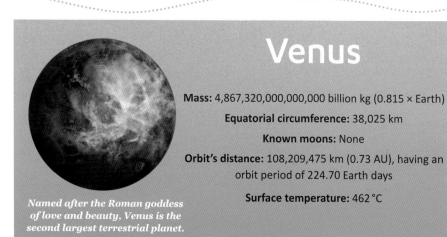

Mass: 4,867,320,000,000,000 billion kg (0.815 × Earth)

Equatorial circumference: 38,025 km

Known moons: None

Orbit's distance: 108,209,475 km (0.73 AU), having an orbit period of 224.70 Earth days

Surface temperature: 462 °C

Named after the Roman goddess of love and beauty, Venus is the second largest terrestrial planet.

FUN FACT

At one point, it was thought that Venus may be a tropical paradise, as the dense clouds of sulphuric acid around it make it impossible to view its surface from outside its atmosphere. It was only later that scientists observed and measured the extreme temperatures and hostile environment.

Appearance

Venus is often referred to as Earth's "sister planet". This is because of their similar mass, size, nearness to the Sun and bulk composition. But, in other respects it is known to be quite different from Earth. Of the four terrestrial planets, Venus has the densest atmosphere made up of more than 96 per cent carbon dioxide. With a surface temperature of 462 °C (735 K), it is by far the hottest planet in the solar system, despite Mercury being the closest one to the Sun. Venus has no carbon cycle that converts carbon into rock, nor does it appear to have any organic life to absorb carbon into biomass.

Early studies

Ancient civilisations knew Venus as the "morning star" and "evening star", based on the assumption that these were two separate objects. The Greeks, too, thought of them as two separate stars, "Phosphorus" and "Hesperus". The Romans named the morning Venus "Lucifer", or Light-Bringer, and the evening one "Vesper". The Babylonians understood that the two were a single object. They referred to it as the "bright queen of the sky" in their tablet.

Atmospheric pressure on Venus is 92 times greater than Earth's.

The planet is bright enough to be seen in a mid-day clear sky and it can be easily seen when the Sun is low on the horizon.

Location and Movement

Venus orbits the Sun at an average distance of about 0.72 AU and completes an orbit every 224.65 days. Although all planetary orbits are elliptical, Venus' orbit is more circular. When viewed from Earth's North Pole, the other planets of the solar system are known to orbit the Sun in an anti-clockwise direction, but Venus rotates clockwise, called "retrograde" rotation, once every 243 Earth days. A Venusian day lasts longer than a Venusian year. The equator of Venus rotates at 6.5 km per hour.

Observation

Venus has no natural satellites, though the asteroid 2002 VE68 presently maintains a quasi-orbital relationship with it. Studies show that Venus is likely to have had at least one moon created by a huge-impact event billions of years ago. The study goes on to state that another impact occurred about 10 million years later that reversed the planet's spin direction. It caused Venus' moon to slowly spiral inward until it finally collided and merged with Venus.

Venusian phases

As it moves around its orbit, Venus displays phases like those of the moon in a telescopic view. When the planet is on the opposite side of the Sun, it presents a small "full" phase . When at its maximum elongations from the Sun, Venus shows a larger "quarter phase" and is at its brightest in the night sky. It presents a much larger "thin crescent" in telescopic views as it comes around to the nearer side, between Earth and the Sun.

Due to retrograde rotation on Venus, the Sun rises in the West.

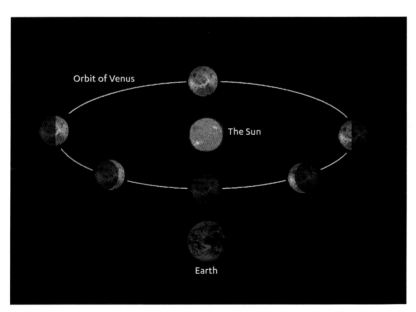

▲ *The different phases of Venus as seen from Earth. Just like the moon, the Sun illuminates parts of Venus as it orbits around it.*

Surface of Venus

Venus has very high atmospheric pressure, low winds and very high temperatures. This is the reason why the surface of Venus can be called rocky. From a distance, the planet looks like any other planet. However, owing to the Soviet Union's Venera 13 lander, we were able to take a closer look at the surface of Venus. Although covered by clouds, there is a good amount of sunlight that shines through and lights up the surface. To be precise, the surface of Venus is flat and slabby. This is not unlike the sedimentary rocks present on Earth that are naturally layered. However, what has caused the land of Venus to become that way is yet to be discovered.

Transit of Venus

A transit of Venus across the Sun occurs when the planet Venus passes directly between the Sun and Earth (or another planet), becoming visible against the solar disc. During a transit, Venus can be seen from Earth as a small black disc moving across the face of the Sun. The duration of such transits is usually measured in hours. It is similar to a solar eclipse caused by the moon. The reason why Venus appears smaller and travels slowly across the surface of the Sun, is because it is further away from the Earth.

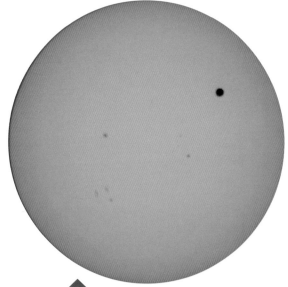

▲
Transits of Venus are among the rarest of predictable astronomical phenomena. We see the shadow of Venus falling on the Sun.

Scientific importance

Venus transits are, historically, of great scientific importance since they were used to obtain the first accurate estimates of the solar system's size. Observing the 1639 transit, along with the principle of parallax has given an estimate of the distance between the Sun and Earth with greater accuracy than any other till that period. The 2012 transit provided scientists with several research opportunities, especially to refine the techniques that are used to explore exoplanets (planets that are outside our solar system).

Ancient history

Observers from Greek, Egypt, Ancient India, Babylon and China knew about Venus and had recorded the motions of the planet. The early Greek astronomers called Venus by two names—Hesperus, or the evening star and Phosphorus which was the morning star. Pythagoras has been given the credit of recognizing them to be the same planet. There is no evidence that any of these cultures knew of the transits.

The eight-year itch

Currently, transits occur only in June or December and the occurrence of these

▲
People watching Venus Transit at the David Dunlap Observatory on 5th June, 2012, in Richmond Hill, Ontario, Canada.

◀ *Diagram of Venus transits.*

events slowly drifts, getting delayed each year by about two days every 243-year cycle. Transits usually take place in pairs. They occur on almost the same date but eight years apart. The reason being, the length of eight years on Earth is nearly the same as 13 years on Venus. Hence, every eight years, the planets are in approximately the same relative positions.

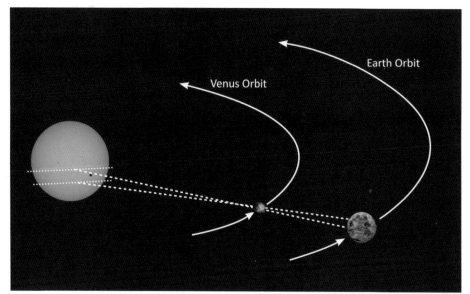

Earth Orbit

Venus Orbit

Earth

Earth is the third planet from the Sun. It is the largest of the terrestrial planets of the inner solar system, bigger than Mercury, Venus and Mars.

Earth's dimensions

The mean distance of Earth from the Sun is 1.49504 km. Earth's mean radius is 36,371 km. However, Earth is not quite round in shape. The planet's rotation causes it to bulge at the equator. Its equatorial diameter is 12,756 km, whereas from pole to pole, the diameter is 12,720 km; a difference of only 64 km.

Earth's circumference and density

Earth's circumference at the equator is about 40,075 km, but from pole-to-pole, it is only 40,008 km around. This shape, caused by the flattening at the poles, is called an "oblate spheroid". Earth's density is 5.52 g/cm³. Its rocky mantle and metallic core make it the densest planet in the solar system. Jupiter, which is 318 times bigger than Earth, is less dense because it is made up of gases, such as hydrogen.

Earth's mass and volume

Earth's mass is 5.9722×1024 kg and its volume is 1.08321×1012 km.

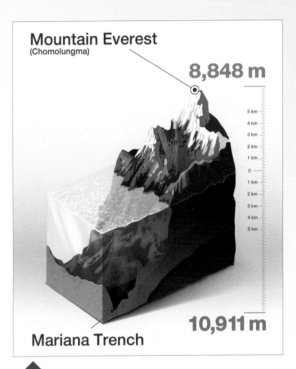

Vector form of the highest and deepest places on Earth.

▼ *The Sun's light takes 8 minutes and 20 seconds to travel to Earth.*

Surface area

The total surface area of Earth is about 509 million km². About 71 per cent, that is 361,000,000 km², is covered by water and 29 per cent, that is 149,000,000 km², by land.

Zenith and Nadir

Mount Everest is the highest place on Earth, that is above sea level, at 29,028 feet (8,848 m), but it is not the highest point on Earth. That title belongs to Mount Chimaborazo in the Andes Mountains in Ecuador.

Mariana Trench, which lies in the western Pacific Ocean, is the lowest point on Earth and is located almost 36,200 feet (11,034 m) below sea level.

Location and Movement

The Earth rotates around an imaginary line, which passes through its North and South poles. This imaginary line is known as the axis of rotation. Earth rotates once a day, approximately 24 hours, on its axis. This rotation results in daytime when an area is facing the Sun and night time when an area is facing away from it. As we are on Earth, we do not sense its rotation, but we experience it by observing the Sun's motion.

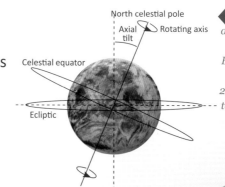

The orbital and axial planes are not precisely aligned: Earth's axis is tilted approximately 23.4° perpendicular to Earth-Sun plane.

Apparent diurnal motion

For an observer at a fixed position on Earth, its rotation makes it appear as if the sky is revolving around Earth. In other words, if you were to stand for a sufficient period of time in a field at night, it would appear like the sky is moving around you.

Earth's orbit

Earth orbits the Sun at a distance of about 150 million km every 365.2564 mean solar days or one sidereal year. Due to this motion, on an average, it takes 24 hours for Earth to complete a full rotation about its axis. When viewed from a vantage point above the North poles of both the Sun and Earth, Earth orbits in a counter-clockwise direction around the Sun.

Axial tilt and seasons

Due to Earth's axial tilt, the amount of sunlight reaching any given point on the surface varies over the year. This causes a seasonal change in the climate, with summer in the northern hemisphere occurring when the North Pole is pointing towards the Sun and winter occurring when the pole is pointed away. During summer, the days last longer and the Sun climbs higher in the sky. In winter, the days are shorter.

Above the Arctic Circle, an extreme point is reached where there is no daylight at all for a part of the year. It is dark for up to six months at the North Pole itself and is called a polar night. In the southern hemisphere, the situation is exactly reversed where the direction of the South Pole is oriented opposite to the North Pole.

Seasonal variation.

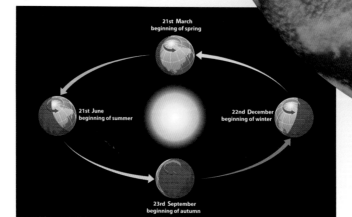

FUN FACT

Without the axial tilt, there would be an eclipse every two weeks, alternating between lunar and solar eclipses.

Earth's Structure

The shape of Earth approximates an oblate spheroid; a sphere which is flattened along the axis from pole to pole such that there is a bulge around the equator. This bulge results from the rotation of Earth, and causes the diameter at the equator to be 43 km larger than the pole-to-pole diameter.

Inner core

It extends another 1,448 km towards the centre of Earth. It is believed that this inner core is a solid ball of, mostly, iron and nickel.

Outer core

It extends to a depth of around 4,828 km beneath the surface. It is believed that this outer core is made up of super-heated molten lava.

Earth's crust

The first layer consists of about 16 km of rock and loose materials that scientists call the crust. Beneath the continents, the crust is almost three times as thick as it is beneath the oceans.

The mantle

It extends to a depth of approximately 2,897 km and is made of a thick, solid, rocky substance that represents about 85 per cent of the total weight and mass of Earth. The first 80 km of the mantle is believed to consist of very hard and rigid rock. The next 241 km is believed to be super-heated solid rock that, due to the heat energy, is very weak.

What Earth is made up of

Earth is made of four distinct layers. These layers are the crust, mantle, outer and inner cores.

Chemical composition

Earth's mass is approximately 5.97×10^{24} kg. It is composed mostly of iron (32.1%), oxygen (30.1%), silicon (15.1%), magnesium (13.9%), sulphur (2.9%), nickel (1.8%), calcium (1.5%) and aluminium (1.4%), and the remaining 1.2% consists of trace amounts of other elements. Due to mass segregation, Earth's core is understood to be primarily made up of iron (88.8%), with small quantities of sulphur (4.5%), nickel (5.8%), and less than 1% trace elements.

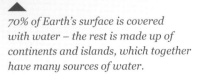

70% of Earth's surface is covered with water – the rest is made up of continents and islands, which together have many sources of water.

How Earth was Formed

Earth, the only planet known to support life was formed approximately 4.54 billion years ago. Although scientists estimate that over 99 per cent of all species that ever lived on the planet are extinct, currently 10–14 million species of life call Earth their home, including over 7.2 billion humans, who depend upon its biosphere and minerals.

FUN FACT

Earth is the only planet not named after a Roman god or goddess.

Formation of the solar system.

Formation

The formation and evolution of the solar system occurred along with the Sun. In theory, a solar nebula partitioned a volume out of a molecular cloud due to gravitational collapse, which began to spin and flatten into a circum-stellar disc, and then the planets grew out of that along with the star. A nebula contains gas, ice grains and dust. The assembly of the primordial Earth proceeded for 10–20 million years. The moon formed shortly thereafter, approximately 4.53 billion years ago.

Geological history

Earth's atmosphere and oceans are formed by volcanic activity, and outgassing that included water vapour. The origin of the world's oceans could have occurred due to an increase in the condensation of water and ice from proto-planets, asteroids and comets. Around 3.5 billion years ago, Earth's magnetic field was established, which helped prevent the atmosphere from being stripped away by solar winds. A crust formed when the molten outer layer of Earth cooled to form a solid, as the water vapour accumulated in the atmosphere.

Formation of continents

Continents were formed by plate tectonics, a process eventually driven by the continuous loss of heat from Earth's interior. In the last hundreds of millions of years, the supercontinents have formed and broken up thrice. Roughly 750 million years ago, one of the earliest known supercontinents, Rodinia, began to break apart. The continents later joined to form Pannotia, 540–600 million years ago, then finally Pangaea, which also broke apart 180 million years ago.

As the continents move around, they sometimes hit each other, creating mountains. This is how the Alps and the Himalayas were created.

▼ *An old world map.*

CONTINENTAL DRIFT

Pangaea

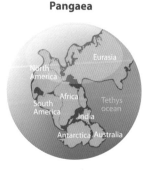

Laurasia and Gondwana

Modern world

Earth's History

 It seems impossible to imagine an Earth without any life on it. Millions of years ago, Earth was lifeless. And then, unicellular beings began to exist. They were formed in water. From single-celled to multi-celled to beings with complex cellular structures, Earth has come a long way and so have humans, along with it.

Beginning of life

The first life forms appeared between 3.5 and 3.8 billion years ago. Life remained mostly small and microscopic until about 580 million years ago, when complex multi-cellular life started appearing.

Geological changes have been taking place continuously on Earth from the time of its formation. Biological changes have occured, since the time life first appeared. Species constantly evolve, taking on new forms, splitting into daughter species or going extinct in response to an ever-changing planet.

Hadean and Archean eons

The first eon during Earth's history, the Hadean, begins with Earth's formation and is followed by the Archean eon at 3.8 Ga. The oldest rocks found on Earth date to about 4.0 Ga, soon after the formation of Earth's crust and Earth itself. By the beginning of the Archean, Earth had significantly cooled. Most of the present life forms could not have survived in the Archean atmosphere, which lacked oxygen and also an ozone layer.

Formation of the moon

Earth's one and only natural satellite, the moon, is a larger relative of its planet than any other satellite in the solar system. Radiometric dating of rocks from the moon has shown that it was formed at least 60 million years after the solar system.

Origin of life

The first step in the appearance of life may have been chemical reactions that produced many of the simpler organic compounds, including amino acids, which are the building blocks of life.

The subsequent stage of complexity could have been reached from at least three possible starting points: self-replication, metabolism and external cell membranes. This allows the food to enter and waste products to exit, but excludes unwanted substances.

Geochronological scale
millions of years ago

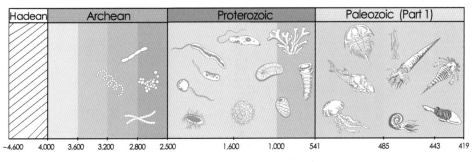

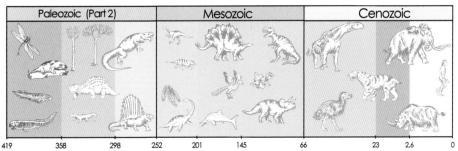

Earth's Atmosphere

Earth's atmosphere is a thin layer of gases that surrounds it. It is composed of 78 per cent nitrogen, 21 per cent oxygen, 0.9 per cent argon, 0.03 per cent carbon dioxide and trace amounts of other gases. This thin layer insulates Earth from extreme temperatures; keeping heat within the atmosphere and also blocking it from the Sun's incoming ultraviolet radiation.

Earth's ability to support life depends on its atmosphere.

1 Exosphere

The exosphere is the outermost layer of Earth's atmosphere. The exosphere being from about 640 to 1,280 km above Earth.

4 Ionosphere

The ionosphere starts at about 70–80 km above Earth and continues for hundreds of kilometres (640 km). It contains many ions and free electrons (plasma). The ions are created when sunlight hits the atoms and strips off some of its electrons.

5 Stratosphere

The stratosphere is characterised by a slight temperature increase with height and the absence of clouds. The stratosphere extends from 16 to 50 km above Earth's surface. The ozone layer is located in the stratosphere. This layer absorbs a lot of ultraviolet solar energy.

2 Thermosphere

The thermosphere is a thermal classification of the atmosphere. In the thermosphere, the temperature increases with the altitude.

3 Mesosphere

The mesosphere is characterised by temperatures that quickly decrease as the height increases. The mesosphere extends from 17 to 80 km above Earth's surface.

Formation of the atmosphere

Earth's atmosphere was formed by planetary degassing, a process in which gases like carbon dioxide, water vapour, sulphur dioxide and nitrogen were released from its interior from volcanoes and other processes. Life forms on Earth have modified the composition of the atmosphere since their evolution.

Northern lights (aurora borealis) in the night sky over a lake.

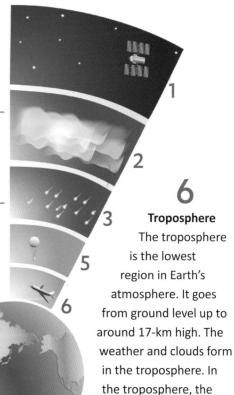

6 Troposphere

The troposphere is the lowest region in Earth's atmosphere. It goes from ground level up to around 17-km high. The weather and clouds form in the troposphere. In the troposphere, the temperature generally decreases as the altitude increases.

Life on Earth

 A "habitable" planet is one that can sustain life even if life did not originate on it. Earth provides liquid water—an environment where complex organic molecules can assemble and interact, and there is sufficient energy to sustain metabolism. Factors that contribute to the current climatic conditions on the surface of the Earth include—Earth's distance from the Sun, its sustaining atmosphere, orbital eccentricity, the rate at which the Earth rotates, axial tilt, geological history, and its protective magnetic field.

The biosphere

Life is everywhere on Earth; you can find living organisms from the poles to the equator, at the bottom of the sea to several miles in the air, from freezing waters to dry valleys to undersea thermal vents to groundwater thousands of feet below Earth's surface. Over the last 3.7 billion years or so, living organisms on Earth have diversified and adapted to almost every environment imaginable.

Human geography

It is estimated that one-eighth of Earth's surface is suitable for humans to live on. Three quarters of it is covered by oceans, leaving one quarter as land. Half of that land area is desert (14 per cent), high mountains (27 per cent) or other unsuitable terrain.

Natural resources and land use

Large deposits of fossil fuels are obtained from Earth's crust, consisting of coal, petroleum and natural gas. Earth's biosphere produces many biological products for humans, including food, wood, pharmaceuticals and oxygen.

▼ *Humans can use only about .003 per cent of the water on Earth.*

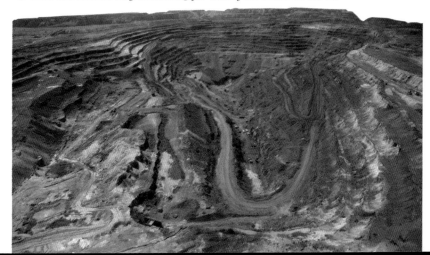

Natural and environmental hazards

Large areas of Earth's surface are subject to extreme weather, such as tropical cyclones, hurricanes or typhoons. Many places are subject to earthquakes, landslides, tsunamis, volcanic eruptions, floods, droughts and other calamities. Many areas are subject to pollution, acid rain, loss of vegetation and erosion.

The most distant point from the centre of Earth is a volcano.

▼

FUN FACT

In the past, Earth was believed to be flat. However, spherical Earth, a concept that has been credited to Pythagoras, displaced this.

Mars

In the night sky, you can sometimes see a very bright star that shines with a reddish twinkle. This star is actually the planet Mars. It is the fourth planet from the Sun and lies at a distance of about 228 million km. It is the second smallest planet in the solar system, after Mercury. It is named after the Roman god of war. Interestingly, some parts of this planet look similar to the moon.

Mars

Mass: 641,693,000,000,000 billion kg (0.107 × Earth)

Equatorial diameter: 6,805

Equatorial circumference: 21,297 km

Notable moons: Phobos and Deimos

Orbit period: 686.98 Earth days (1.88 Earth years)

Surface temperature: -87 to -5 °C

It is described as the "Red Planet", because the iron oxide prevalent on its surface gives it a reddish appearance.

Internal structure

A silicate mantle that formed many tectonic and volcanic features on the planet surrounds the core, but it now appears to be dormant. Besides silicon and oxygen, the other abundant elements in the Martian crust are iron, magnesium, aluminium, calcium and potassium. The average thickness of the planet's crust is about 50 km, with a maximum thickness of 125 km as compared to the 40-km crust of Earth.

Etymology

The planet of Mars gets its name from the Roman god of war. In various cultures, Mars represents masculinity and youth. Its symbol, which is a circle with an arrow pointing out to the upper right, is also used as a symbol to denote the male gender.

Physical characteristics

Mars has approximately half the diameter of Earth. Its surface area is only slightly less than Earth's dry land. Even though Mars is larger and has more mass than Mercury, Mercury has a higher density. This evens them out and makes the two planets have an almost similar gravitational pull at the surface.

The reddish appearance of the Martian surface is caused by iron oxide, more commonly known as hematite, or rust. It sometimes also looks like butterscotch, or golden, brown, tan and greenish, depending on the minerals.

Location and Movement

Mars takes 687 days to orbit the Sun. It travels 9.55 AU in doing so, making its average orbital speed 24 km per second. As Earth completes its 24-hour-per-day spin, it results in the Coriolis "force". Earth is 40,000 km around at its widest part, the equator. Because it spins on its axis once in 24 hours, a point on its equator is moving about 1700 km per hour in relation to its axis.

Mars in its orbit, fourth planet from the Sun.

Mars is visible from Earth

Mars reaches an opposition when there is a 180-degree difference between its geocentric longitudes and that of the Sun. Every opposition has some significance because Mars becomes visible from Earth, all night, high and fully lit, but the ones of special interest occur when Mars is near the perihelion, because this is when it is also the closest to Earth.

Laws of planetary motion

German astronomer Johannes Kepler formulated three laws of planetary motion. A key discovery was that the motion of Mars followed an elliptical path. This happened because his model with a circular orbit did not match the observations of Mars.

Surface geology

Mars is one of the terrestrial planets and consists of minerals containing silicon and oxygen, metals, and other elements that rocks are ideally made of. The surface of Mars is primarily composed of tholeiitic basalt. Parts of the southern moorland include noticeable amounts of high-calcium pyroxenes. Localised concentrations of hematite and olivine have also been found. Quite a lot of the surface is deeply covered by fine iron oxide dust.

Martian soil has a basic pH of 7.7 and contains 0.6 per cent of salt perchlorate.

Martian soil

Martian soil is slightly alkaline and contains elements, such as magnesium, sodium, potassium and chlorine. These nutrients, necessary for plant growth, are found in the gardens on Earth.

Streaks across Mars are common and new ones frequently appear on steep slopes of craters, troughs and valleys. The streaks are dark at first and get lighter as they age. They have also been seen to follow the edges of boulders and other obstacles in their path.

Hydrology

Liquid water cannot exist on Mars due to its low atmospheric pressure, which is about 100 times thinner than Earth's, although, the polar ice caps seem to be made mainly of water.

FUN FACT

The amount of water ice in the south polar ice cap of Mars, if melted, would be sufficient to cover the entire surface up to a depth of 11 m.

Geology and Atmosphere

During the solar system's formation, Mars was created as a result of run-away accretion out of the proto-planetary disc that orbited the Sun. Mars has typical chemical features due to its position in the solar system. Elements with relatively low boiling points, such as chlorine, phosphorus and sulphur, are much more common on Mars than Earth.

Polar caps

Mars has two permanent polar ice caps. During winter at the pole, it is in continuous darkness, chilling the surface and converting the atmosphere into dry ice. When the poles are exposed to sunlight, the frozen CO_2 evaporates, creating enormous winds that sweep off the poles as fast as 400 km per hour.

These seasonal actions move huge amounts of dust and water vapour, giving rise to frost and large cirrus clouds, like on Earth.

Martian atmosphere

The solar winds interact directly with the ionosphere of Mars. The removal of atoms from the outer layer, lowers the atmospheric density. The atmospheric pressure on the surface ranges from 0.030 kPa on Olympus Mons to over 1.155 kPa in Hellas Planitia.

Atmospheric make up

The atmosphere of Mars comprises about 96 per cent carbon dioxide, 1.93 per cent argon and 1.89 per cent nitrogen with traces of oxygen and water. The atmosphere is rather dusty, containing particulates about 1.5 μm in diameter that gives the Martian sky an orange colour when observed from the surface of Earth.

▼ *Dust storm on Mars.*

The atmospheric density of the planet of Mars is lowered because of the impact that the solar winds have on it.

Seasons of Mars

The seasons of Mars are similar to Earth's. The lengths of the seasons are about twice those of Earth's because Mars is farther from the Sun causing the Martian year to be around two Earth years long. Martian surface temperatures vary from about −143 to 35 °C. Mars also has the largest dust storms in the solar system. These vary from a storm over a small area, to massive storms covering the planet entirely. They tend to occur when Mars is the closest to the Sun and lead to increased global temperature.

FUN FACT

The shield volcano Olympus Mons is an extinct volcano in the vast upland region of Tharsis. Mount Olympus is approximately three times the height of Mount Everest.

Transit of Earth From Mars

A transit of Earth across the Sun as seen from Mars occurs when the planet Earth passes directly between the Sun and Mars, obscuring a small part of the Sun's disc for an observer on Mars. When a transit occurs, Earth, if viewed from Mars, would be visible as a small black disc moving across the surface of the Sun.

View from Mars

No one has ever seen a transit of Earth from Mars, but the next transit will take place on 10th November, 2084. The last transit of this type took place on 11th May, 1984. If viewed from Mars, during the event, it is possible for even the moon to be visible. However, the distance between Earth and its moon is such that they end up finishing their transits at different points in time.

When viewed from Mars, the moon becomes visible during transit.

During the transit, Earth passes between the Sun and Mars.

View from Earth

A transit of Earth from Mars corresponds to Mars being perfectly and uniformly illuminated opposite Earth. More recently, using a radar from Earth has made better measurements of the oblateness of Mars possible. Also, better measurements have been made using artificial satellites that have been put into the orbit around Mars, including Mariner 9, Viking 1, Viking 2 and Soviet orbiters. These are the more recent orbiters that have been sent from Earth to Mars.

Grazing and simultaneous transits

Sometimes, Earth only grazes the Sun during a transit. When this occurs, there is a possibility of seeing a full transit from some areas of Mars. In other regions there is only a partial transit (no second or third contact). It is also possible that a transit of Earth can be seen from some parts of Mars as a partial transit, while in others, Earth misses the Sun.

Position of the Sun, Moon and Mars during the transit.

FUN FACT

The simultaneous occurrence of a transit of Venus and Earth is extremely rare, and will next occur in the year 571,471.

Jupiter

Jupiter is the fifth planet from the Sun and it is the largest planet in the solar system. With one-thousandth the mass of the Sun, Jupiter, is one of the gas giants. However, it is two and a half times the total mass of the other planets in the solar system combined together. When observed from Earth, Jupiter can reach an apparent magnitude of −2.94, that is adequately bright to cast shadows.

Jupiter

Mass: 1,898,130,000,000,000,000 billion kg (317.83 x Earth)

Equatorial circumference: 439,264 km

Known moons: 67

Notable moons: Io, Europa, Ganymede and Callisto

Known rings: 4

Orbit period: 4,332.82 Earth days (11.86 Earth years)

The Romans named the planet after the roman God Jupiter.

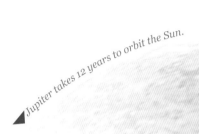

Jupiter takes 12 years to orbit the Sun.

Etymology

The Romans named the planet after the Roman god Jupiter. To the Greeks, it represented Zeus, the god of thunder. For the Mesopotamians, Jupiter was the god Marduk and a patron of the city of Babylon. Germanic tribes saw this planet as Thor.

Earth overtakes Jupiter every 398.9 days as it orbits the Sun. This duration is called the synodic period. As it does so, Jupiter appears to undergo retrograde motion with respect to the background stars, that is, for a period, Jupiter seems to move backward in the night sky, performing a loop in its motion.

Zodiac relation

Jupiter's 12-year orbital period can be related to the dozen astrological signs of the zodiac. It may have been responsible for the historical origin of the signs. Every time the planet reaches opposition, it has advanced eastward by about 30°, which is the width of a zodiac sign.

The illumination of Jupiter

Because the orbit of Jupiter is outside that of Earth's, the planet always appears nearly fully illuminated when viewed through Earth-based telescopes. Crescent views of Jupiter were acquired only during spacecraft missions to the planet. A small telescope will usually show Jupiter's four Galilean moons and the prominent cloud belts across Jupiter's atmosphere. A large telescope can show Jupiter's Great Red Spot when it faces Earth.

▼ *Jupiter as compared to Earth.*

EARTH

JUPITER

FUN FACT

Jupiter has the shortest day when compared to the other seven planets. It orbits the Sun once every 11.8 Earth years.

Location and Movement

Jupiter is the only planet that has a centre of mass with the Sun that lies outside its volume, though by only seven per cent of the Sun's radius. The average distance between Jupiter and the Sun is 778 million km. The elliptical orbit of Jupiter is inclined 1.31 degrees compared to Earth. This planet does not experience significant seasonal changes, in contrast to Earth and Mars, as its axial tilt is relatively small.

It is the third brightest object in the night sky after the moon and Venus.

Fastest rotation

Jupiter's rotation is the fastest amongst all the planets in our solar system. It completes a rotation on its axis in a little less than 10 hours, creating an equatorial bulge easily seen through an amateur telescope.
The planet is shaped as an oblate spheroid; this means that the diameter across its equator is longer than that between its poles. Since Jupiter is not a solid body, the rotation of Jupiter's polar atmosphere is about five minutes longer than its equatorial atmosphere.

Magnetosphere

Jupiter's magnetic field is 14 times as strong as Earth's, ranging from 0.42 metric tonne at the equator to 1.0–1.4 metric tonne at the poles, making it the strongest in the solar system. This magnetic field is said to have been formed from eddy currents (swirling movements of conducting materials) inside the core of liquid metallic hydrogen.

Formation of a magneto-disc

The gas ionised in the magnetosphere produces sulphur and oxygen ions, together with hydrogen ions. This forms a plasma sheet in Jupiter's equatorial plane. The plasma in the sheet rotates along with the planet, deforming the dipole magnetic field into that of a magneto-disc.

The four largest moons of Jupiter orbit within this magnetosphere, which protects them from the solar wind.

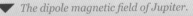
The dipole magnetic field of Jupiter.

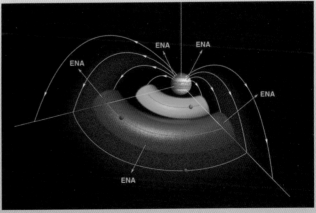

Atmosphere and Surface

Jupiter is composed chiefly of gaseous and liquid matter. It is the biggest of four gas giants and also the largest planet in the solar system. The density of Jupiter, 1.326 g/cm³, is lower than any of the four terrestrial planets.

Composition

Jupiter's upper atmosphere is composed of about 88–92 per cent hydrogen and 8–12 per cent helium by per cent volume of gas molecules.

The atmosphere is about 75 per cent hydrogen and 24 per cent helium by mass; the remaining 1 per cent of the mass consists of other elements. The interior contains denser materials so that the distribution is roughly 71 per cent hydrogen, 24 per cent helium and 5 per cent other elements by mass. The atmosphere contains trace amounts of methane, water vapour, ammonia and silicon-based compounds. Traces of carbon, oxygen, ethane, neon, hydrogen sulphide, sulphur and phosphine are also found. Crystals of frozen ammonia are found in the outermost layer of its atmosphere.

Jupiter's layers.

Rocky core

Jupiter is believed to have a dense core consisting of a mixture of elements. This is surrounded by a layer of liquid metallic hydrogen with a little helium. The outer layer mainly contains molecular hydrogen. The core is often described as rocky, but its detailed composition is unknown.

Planetary rings

Jupiter has a faint planetary ring system of three main segments. It has an inner "torus" of particles called the halo, a comparatively bright main ring and an outer gossamer ring. These rings seem to be made of dust, instead of ice. The main ring is probably made of material expelled from the satellites, Adrastea and Metis. Due to its strong gravitational influence, material that would usually fall back on the moon is pulled into Jupiter.

Great Red Spot

Latest evidence by the Hubble Space Telescope shows that there are three "red spots" adjacent to the Great Red Spot. Mathematical models suggest that the storm is stable and could be a permanent characteristic of Jupiter. The storm is sufficiently large to be seen through Earth-based telescopes.

FUN FACT

The Great Red Spot is a huge storm on Jupiter that has raged for at least 350 years. It is so huge that three Earths could fit within it.

◀ *The planetary rings of Jupiter: The Inner halo, the bright main ring and the outer gossamer ring.*

Saturn

Saturn is the sixth planet from the Sun and the second largest planet in the solar system, after Jupiter. It is named after the Roman god of agriculture; its astronomical symbol represents the god's sickle. Saturn is a gas giant with an average radius around nine times that of Earth. One-eighth the average density of Earth, Saturn is just over 95 times bigger.

Saturn

Mass: 568,319,000,000,000,000 billion kg (95.16 x Earth)

Equatorial circumference: 365,882 km

Known moons: 62

Notable moons: Titan, Rhea and Enceladus

Known rings: 30+ (7 groups)

Orbit period: 10,755.70 Earth days (29.45 Earth years)

Surface temperature: −139 °C

Saturn is named after the Roman god of agriculture.

FUN FACT

Saturn has the most extensive rings in the solar system, which are mainly made of chunks of ice and carbonaceous dust. The rings from Saturn, extend more than 120,700 km from the planet. However, they are surprisingly thin; only about 20-m thick.

One of the giant

Saturn is one of the giant planets in our solar system. It is oblate in shape, meaning that it is wider around the equator. It spins very fast, completing its rotation every 10.7 hours. Material is flung in an outward direction as it spins, which gives it a bulging equator. It is the least dense planet. Interestingly, if Saturn was to be placed in a huge ocean of water, it would float!

Saturn's rings

Saturn has a prominent ring system that consists of nine continuous main rings and three discontinuous arcs, composed chiefly of ice particles and some rocky debris and dust. The planet is orbited by 62 moons; out of which 53 are officially named. This does not include the multiple "moonlets" comprising the rings. Titan, Saturn's largest moon and the solar system's second largest moon is bigger than Mercury, and is the only moon in the solar system to hold its own atmosphere.

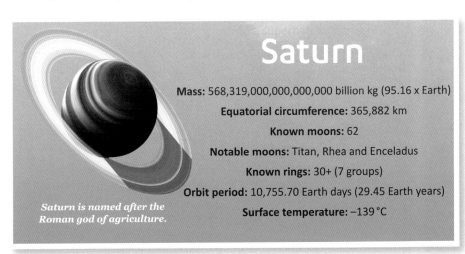

Virtual image of Saturn and its rings. ▼

Occultation by the moon

Saturn is the farthest of the five planets that are easily visible to the naked eye.

The other four are Mercury, Venus, Mars and Jupiter. Saturn appears to the naked eye in the night sky as a bright, yellowish point of light. Twice every Saturnian year (approximately every 15 Earth years), the rings temporarily disappear from view, due to their angle and thinness. Periodically, the moon occults Saturn, that is, the moon completely covers Saturn in the sky.

◀ *Comparison between Saturn and Earth.*

Location and Movement

The average distance between Saturn and the Sun is over 1.4 billion km (9 AU). It takes Saturn 10,759 Earth days (or about 29.4 years), to finish one revolution around the Sun. Depending on the latitude, the features seen on Saturn rotate at different rates. Various regions have been assigned multiple rotation periods.

Saturn's rotational pattern

The latest estimate of Saturn's rotation (as an indicated rotation rate for the whole of Saturn), based on a compilation of various measurements, is 10 hours, 32 minutes and 35 seconds.

The gaseous giant

Saturn is termed as a gaseous giant because its exterior is chiefly composed of gas and it lacks a definite surface, although it may have a solid core. The rotation of the planet makes it take the shape of an oblate spheroid. Its equatorial and polar radii differ by almost 10 per cent. Saturn is the only planet in the solar system that is less dense than water (about 30 per cent less). Although Saturn's core is significantly denser than water, the average specific density of the planet is less due to the gaseous atmosphere.

Magnetosphere

Saturn has an intrinsic magnetic field that is a magnetic dipole. Its strength at the equator is approximately $1/20^{th}$ of the field around Jupiter and slightly weaker than Earth's magnetic field. As a result, Saturn's magnetosphere is much smaller than Jupiter's. The magnetosphere is efficient at deflecting the solar wind particles from the Sun. The moon, Titan, that orbits it is in the outer part of Saturn's magnetosphere and contributes plasma from the ionised particles in Titan's outer atmosphere. Saturn's magnetosphere produces auroras, just like Earth.

Saturn is also known as the gaseous giant as it is majorly made of gases.

FUN FACT

Saturn orbits the Sun once every 29.4 Earth years. Due to its slow movement against the backdrop of stars, it got the nickname of "Lubadsagush" from the ancient Assyrians, which means "oldest of the old".

Atmosphere and Surface

Saturn is termed as a gas giant, but it is not completely gaseous. The temperature, pressure and density inside the planet rise steadily towards the core, which causes hydrogen to convert into a metal in the deeper layers of the planet.

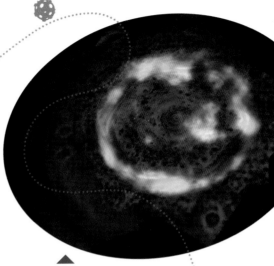

The planet chiefly consists of hydrogen.

Internal structure

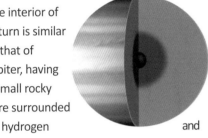

The interior of Saturn is similar to that of Jupiter, having a small rocky core surrounded by hydrogen and helium with small amounts of various volatile substances. This core is also similar in composition to Earth, but denser. The core is about 9–22 times the mass of Earth. A thicker liquid layer of metallic hydrogen, followed by a layer of liquid helium-saturated molecular hydrogen that slowly transitions into gas with increasing altitude, surrounds this. The outermost layer spans 1,000 km and consists of a gaseous atmosphere.

Atmosphere

The outer atmosphere of Saturn contains 96.3 per cent molecular hydrogen and 3.25 per cent helium by volume. The proportion of helium is significantly deficient compared to the abundance of this element present in the Sun. The quantity of elements heavier than helium is not precisely known, but the proportions are assumed to match the primordial abundances from the solar system formation. The total mass of these heavier elements is assessed to be 19–31 times Earth's mass, with a substantial fraction located in the core region of Saturn.

Shepherd moons

Saturn is best known for the system of planetary rings that make it visually unique. The rings extend from 6,630 km to 120,700 km above its equator and are approximately 20 m thick. They are composed of 93 per cent water ice with traces of tholin impurities and 7 per cent amorphous carbon. Beyond the main rings, at a distance of 12 million km from the planet, is the thin Phoebe ring that orbits in retrograde fashion. Some of Saturn's moons, along with Pandora and Prometheus, act as shepherd moons to confine the rings and prevent them from spreading out.

A few moons on the outer edge of Saturn's rings keep the rings from expanding and are known as shepherd moons.

◀ *The other gas giants also have ring systems, but Saturn's is the largest and most visible.*

FUN FACT

Saturn has a hot interior, reaching 11,700 °C at the core, and the planet radiates 2.5 times more energy into space than it receives from the Sun.

Uranus

Uranus is the seventh planet, in terms of distance, from the Sun and it is the third-largest planet in the solar system. Uranus also has the fourth-largest planetary mass. Its atmosphere, with its primary composition of hydrogen and helium, although similar to Jupiter's and Saturn's , contains more "ices" like ammonia, water and methane. It is the planet with the coldest atmosphere in the solar system, with a minimum temperature of 49 K and has a complex, layered cloud structure. The interior of Uranus is mainly composed of ices and rock.

Uranus

Mass: 86,810,300,000,000,000 billion kg (14.536 × Earth)

Equatorial circumference: 159,354 km

Known moons: 27

Notable moons: Oberon, Titania, Miranda, Ariel and Umbriel

Known rings: 13

Orbit distance: 2,870,658,186 km (19.22 AU)

Surface temperature: -197 °C

The Greek god of the sky, Uranus, was the inspiration behind naming this planet.

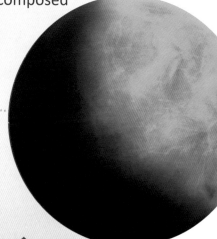

A rendering of the gas planet Uranus in a clear night sky.

All about Uranus

It is four times the size of Earth. Similar to other giant planets, it does not have a solid surface. Its surface is visible due to the layers of methane ice clouds present in its hydrogen-rich atmosphere. The methane gas present in the atmosphere absorbs the red wavelengths in sunlight, which makes the planet appear blue. Like other giant planets, Uranus has a ring system, a magnetosphere and numerous moons. The Uranian system has a distinctive configuration among other planets because its axis of rotation is tilted sideways. Its north and south poles, therefore, lie where most other planets have their equators.

Etymology

Uranus is named after the ancient Greek deity of the sky Ouranus, the father of Cronus (Saturn) and grandfather of Zeus (Jupiter). It is the only planet whose name is derived from a figure of Greek mythology and not Roman mythology.

Smallest giant planet

Uranus' mass is around 14.5 times that of Earth, making it the smallest of the giant planets. It is the second least dense planet, after Saturn. This indicates that it is mainly made of various ices, such as water, ammonia and methane. Hydrogen and helium constitute only a small part of the total (0.5–1.5 Earth masses).

Sir William Herschel discovered Uranus on 13th March, 1781.

FUN FACT

Uranus rotates in a retrograde direction, opposite to the way Earth and most other planets rotate.

Location and Movement

The average distance of Uranus from the Sun is around three billion km (about 20 AU). The variation of that distance is greater than that of any other planet, at 1.8 AU. The intensity of sunlight reduces quadratically with distance, and therefore, the intensity of light on Uranus is about 1/400th the intensity of light on Earth.

Rotation

The rotational period of the interior of Uranus is 17 hours, 14 minutes, clockwise (retrograde). Its upper atmosphere experiences strong winds in the direction of rotation. At some latitudes visible features of the atmosphere move much faster, making a full rotation in as less as 14 hours.

Axial tilt

Uranus has an axial tilt of 98 degrees, so its axis of rotation is approximately parallel with the plane of the solar system. This causes seasonal changes completely unlike those of the other major planets. Other planets can be thought to rotate like a tilted spinning top on the plane of the solar system, but Uranus rotates more like a tilted rolling ball. Each pole gets around 42 years of continuous sunlight, followed by 42 years of darkness. Uranus is hotter at its equator than at its poles.

Axial tilt of Uranus

-59°

Visibility

At opposition, Uranus can be seen with the naked eye in dark skies and can be easily observed, using binoculars, even in urban areas. In larger amateur telescopes, Uranus appears as a pale cyan disc with distinct limb darkening. With a large telescope, cloud patterns, as well as some of the larger satellites, such as Titania and Oberon, may become visible.

Uranus appears blue to us when observed from Earth.

Unlike other planets, Uranus orbits the Sun on its side.

FUN FACT

Uranus makes one trip around the Sun every 84 Earth years.

Atmosphere and Surface

Uranus is a ball of ice and gas. If you tried to land a spacecraft on Uranus, it would just sink through the upper atmosphere of hydrogen and helium into its liquid icy centre. The peculiar orientation of the planet, which orbits the Sun tipped on its side, divulges that its inner core has a stronger influence on its weather patterns than the distant star. When we observe Uranus, we see the blue-green colour that comes from its surface. This colour is the light from the Sun that is reflected off its surface.

Upper Atmosphere
(cloud tops)

Mantle
(water, ammonia,
methane ices)

Core
(rock, ices)

Atmosphere
(hydrogen, helium,
methane gas)

The internal structure of Uranus.

While Uranus appears blue, it has stripes similar to Jupiter and Saturn.

Atmosphere

Uranus' atmosphere includes hydrogen and helium, and most importantly, it has large amounts of methane. This methane absorbs colour in the red end of the spectrum of light, while photons at the blue end of the spectrum are able to reflect off the clouds and go back into space. So, from the full spectrum of the Sun's light, the red and orange end is absorbed. What is reflected back is the blue green end of the spectrum. This is why the surface of Uranus has its colour.

Cloud patterns on Uranus

Although the planet appears blue, it contains stripes like Jupiter and Saturn. However, these bands are faint and are only visible in enhanced images. With respect to other gas giants, the zones are formed as the gases rise in the warm region, while in the belts, the gases fall to the planet as they cool. In the belts, the winds blow east, while they travel west within the zones. In 1986, Voyager 2 flew by the planet only observing 10 cloud patterns on the planet. With improvement in technology, higher resolution images taken from Earth revealed the existence of fainter clouds. The clouds in the troposphere, are carried by winds blowing up to 900 km per hour.

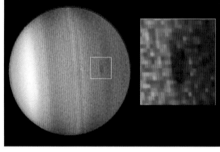

The stripes on Uranus are not visible because of the methane gas clouds that absorb the red light from the sunlight and reflect only the blue spectrum.

FUN FACT

Did you know that Uranus' moons are named after characters created by William Shakespeare and Alexander Pope?

Neptune

Neptune is the eighth planet, in terms of distance, from the Sun. This fourth-largest planet, by diameter, is also the planet which lies farthest from the Sun. It is the third largest by mass. Among the gaseous planets in the solar system, it is the densest. It is 17 times the mass of Earth and orbits the Sun at an average distance of 30.1 AU.

Neptune

Mass: 102,410,000,000,000,000 billion kg (17.15 × Earth)

Equatorial circumference: 155,600 km

Known moons: 14

Notable moons: Triton more info

Known rings: 5

Orbit period: 60,190.03 Earth days (164.79 Earth years)

Surface temperature: -201 °C

The planet is named after the Roman god of the sea

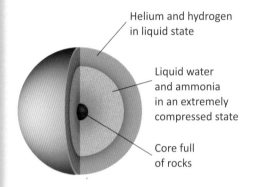

Helium and hydrogen in liquid state

Liquid water and ammonia in an extremely compressed state

Core full of rocks

Ice giant

Neptune's atmosphere is composed primarily of hydrogen and helium, along with traces of hydrocarbons and possibly nitrogen. It is known to contain high proportions of "ices" like water, methane and ammonia. This is why astronomers at times refer to Uranus and Neptune as "ice giants".

The interior of Neptune, like Uranus, is primarily composed of ices and rock. It is possible that the core has a solid surface, however, the temperature would be thousands of degrees. Besides, the atmospheric pressure would be crushing. The planet's blue appearance is due to traces of methane in the outermost regions. In contrast to the hazy, relatively undistinguished atmosphere of Uranus, its atmosphere has active and visible weather patterns.

Neptune is similar in composition to Uranus, and their compositions differ from those of the larger gas giants, Jupiter and Saturn. ▶

Composition

The mass of this planet is midway between Earth and the larger gas giants; it is 17 times that of Earth, but just 1/19th that of Jupiter. Only Jupiter surpasses its surface gravity. Neptune's equatorial radius is nearly four times that of Earth. It has been used as a metonym in search for extrasolar bodies: discovered bodies of similar mass are often referred to as "Neptunes", quite like astronomers refer to various extra-solar bodies as "Jupiters".

Location and Movement

The average distance between Neptune and the Sun is 4.50 billion km (about 30.1 AU). It completes an orbit, on an average, every 164.79 Earth years. The elliptical orbit of Neptune is inclined by 1.77° compared to that of Earth.

Axial tilt

The axial tilt of Neptune is 28.32°, which is similar to the tilts of Earth (23°) and Mars (25°). Therefore, this planet experiences similar seasonal changes. The long orbital period of Neptune means that the seasons last for 40 Earth years.

Orbital resonances

Neptune's orbit has a massive impact on the region that is directly beyond it, known as the Kuiper belt. This belt is a ring of small icy objects which is similar to the asteroid belt, but much larger. Neptune's gravity influences the Kuiper belt. Over the age of the solar system, certain parts of the Kuiper belt were destabilised by Neptune's gravity, creating gaps in the Kuiper belt's structure.

The most heavily populated resonance in the Kuiper belt, having over 200 known objects, is the 2:3 resonance. Objects in this resonance complete two orbits for every three of Neptune and are known as "plutinos", because the largest of the known Kuiper belt objects, Pluto, is among them. Although Pluto crosses Neptune's orbit frequently, the 2:3 resonance ensures that they can never collide. The 3:4, 3:5, 4:7 and 2:5 resonances are less populated.

Trojan objects

A smaller celestial object that shares its orbit with a larger celestial object is called a Trojan object. Neptune possesses a number of Trojan objects occupying the Sun. Neptune Trojans stay in a 1:1 resonance with Neptune. Some Neptune Trojans are particularly stable in their orbits and are more likely to have formed with Neptune rather than being captured. Neptune also has a temporary quasi-satellite. The object has been a quasi-satellite of Neptune for about 12,500 years and will remain so for another 12,500 years, and is likely a captured object.

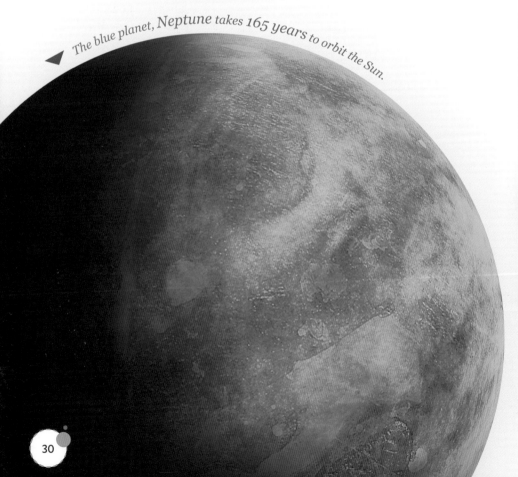

The blue planet, Neptune takes 165 years to orbit the Sun.

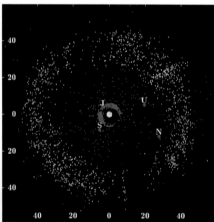

FUN FACT

Neptune has a very thin collection of rings, which are likely made up of ice particles mixed with dust grains and possibly coated with a carbon-based substance.

Atmosphere and Surface

The internal structure of Neptune is similar to that of Uranus and its atmosphere makes up about 5–10 per cent of its mass . It extends around 10–20 per cent of the way towards the core, where it reaches a pressure of about 100,000 times that of the atmosphere of Earth. Increasing amounts of methane, ammonia and water are found in the lower regions of the atmosphere. The core of Neptune is composed of iron, nickel and silicates.

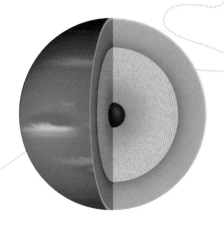

▲ *Neptune's internal structure:*
a. Upper atmosphere-top clouds.
b. Atmosphere consists of gases
(hydrogen, helium, methane).
c. Mantle consists of 'ices ' (ammonia,
methane).
d. Core consists of rocks (silicates and
nickel-iron).

Atmosphere

At high altitudes, Neptune's atmosphere is 80 per cent hydrogen and 19 per cent helium along with a trace amount of methane. Prominent absorption bands of methane occur at wavelengths above 600 nanometre (nm), in the red and infrared portion of the spectrum. Since Neptune's atmospheric methane content is similar to that of Uranus, some unknown atmospheric constituent is thought to contribute to Neptune's colour.

Atmospheric division

Its atmosphere is divided into two regions: the lower troposphere, where the temperature decreases with altitude, and the stratosphere, where the temperature increases with altitude.
The stratosphere gives way to the thermosphere that gradually transitions to the exosphere.

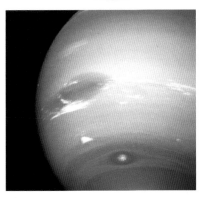

Bands of high-altitude clouds cast shadows
on Neptune's lower cloud deck.
▼

Magnetosphere

Neptune resembles Uranus in its magnetosphere, with a strongly tilted magnetic field. Its magnetic field has an intricate geometry that includes relatively large contributions from non-dipolar components, including a strong quadrupole moment that might exceed the dipole moment in strength; whereas, Earth, Jupiter and Saturn have only relatively small quadrupole moments.

▲
Neptune has very extreme weather
changes that take place on its surface.
It has storms, dark spots and cirruslike
clouds that are bright enough to
be visible through satellite imaging.
Although Neptune receives a thousand
times less sunlight than Earth, it has a
dynamic weather..

FUN FACT

Neptune has a very active climate. Large storms whirl through its upper atmosphere and high-speed winds track around the planet at up to 600 m per second. One of the largest storms ever seen was called the "Great Dark Spot".

Water and Space

Extraterrestrial liquid water is water in its liquid form that is found beyond Earth. It is a subject of wide interest because it is commonly thought to be one of the key prerequisites for the existence of extraterrestrial life. With oceanic water covering 71 per cent of its surface, Earth is the only planet known to have stable bodies of liquid water, which is essential to all known lifeforms.

Scientists using the Hubble telescope have discovered that Jupiter's largest natural satellite, Ganymede, has an ocean buried beneath its icy surface.

▲ *Reservoirs of ice still hidden below Mars' surface*

Icy Mars

The water found on the surface of Mars exists, almost completely, in the form of ice. Small amounts of vapour are present in the atmosphere. Some water, in the liquid form, may be found transiently on the surface of Mars, but only under certain conditions. No large standing bodies of liquid water exist because the atmospheric pressure at the surface averages at just 600 pascals—about 0.6 per cent of Earth's mean sea level pressure—and because the global average temperature is far too low (210 K or −63 °C), it leads to either rapid evaporation or freezing.

Enceladus

Enceladus, a moon of Saturn, has shown geysers of water, confirmed by the Cassini spacecraft in 2005 and analysed more deeply in 2008. Gravimetric data in 2010–11 confirmed a subsurface ocean. Besides water, these geysers also form vents near the South Pole. They contain small quantities of salt, carbon dioxide, nitrogen, and some volatile hydrocarbons. Both the melting of the ocean water and the geysers seem to be driven by tidal flux from Saturn.

Ganymede

A subsurface saline ocean is theorised to exist on Ganymede, a moon of Jupiter, following observation by the Hubble Space Telescope in 2015. Patterns in auroral belts and the rocking of the magnetic field suggest the presence of an ocean. It is estimated to be 100 km deep with the surface lying below a crust of 150 km of ice.

Europa

Scientists' agree that a layer of liquid water exists beneath Europa's surface. Heat from tidal flexing allows this subsurface ocean to remain in the liquid form. It is predicted that the outer crust of solid ice is approximately 10–30 km thick, including a ductile "warm ice" layer, which could mean that the liquid ocean underneath may be about 100 km deep. This puts the volume of Europa's oceans at 3×1018 m³, slightly more than twice the volume of Earth's oceans.

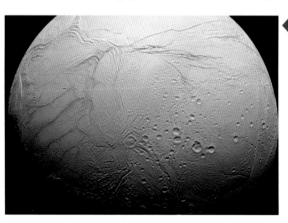

◀ *The blue-green "tiger stripes" are thought to be the source of Enceladus's water jets.*

The icy surface of Europa ▶ *is strewn with cracks, ridges and chaotic terrain, where the surface has been disrupted and ice blocks have moved around.*